Helping Children Understand and Express Emotions.

A practical interoception activity book.

Dr Emma Goodall

ISBN: 978-0-6482800-4-0

978-0-6482800-4-0

DEDICATION

This book is dedicated to all the children and young people and adults who have worked with me or one of my colleagues over the last four years as we have further developed our understanding of how to help you learn to recognize and express your emotions safely.

To the young man who asked if he could teach his mum these strategies, so that she could control his anger, this book came about so that all the other children and young people out there who want to learn alongside their parents can do so easily.

ACKNOWLEDGMENTS

I would like to acknowledge that this book was written on the lands of the Kaurna People, the traditional owners of the Adelaide region and beyond. Kaurna people are amongst those who have participated in the activities in this book to ensure they are indeed useful!

Many thanks to the first followers – you know who you are! I acknowledge the leap of faith that you took and all the hard work that you have put in over the years. I also acknowledge the feedback from my University Supervisor and my whanau and mahi whanau, and the role that has played in the development of this book.

CONTENTS

1 UNDERSTANDING EMOTIONS

WHAT ARE EMOTIONS AND FEELINGS?

We may think of emotions and feelings as a series of emoticons, but what do those actually *feel* like? Feelings are related to biological needs, such as hunger, thirst, sleepy etc, whilst emotions are related to social needs and wants, as represented above. Some children do not understand emoticons, whilst others can tell you what they represent, but do not understand whether that is a pleasant or unpleasant emotion.

If we are thirsty and do not drink, over time our body will get stressed which will impact our emotions and behaviour. Hangry is now widely understood as that angry feeling which occurs when hungry people don't eat. However, many hangry people don't realise they are hungry.

HOW DO YOU FEEL? – ACTIVITY

Try and describe how you are feeling, whether it is an emotion or a feeling. BUT do this only by describing your body signals. There is an example on below:

> My throat is tight, my chest is tight and my hands are clammy...

For many people, especially children and young people, this is very difficult, if not impossible. However, our feelings and emotions are just collections of these types of internal body signals. When we notice our internal body signals, this is our interoceptive awareness. Interoception develops as babies grow into children, however, the development is problematic for lots of children for a variety of reasons.

When our interoception hasn't developed really well, it is very hard for us to recognize and express our emotions and feelings. When this happens, a child might say they are bored, when they are actually tired or frustrated. Unfortunately, if parents and teachers don't understand that the child is not expressing their emotions accurately, they can respond in unhelpful ways.

In addition, when children and young people are not accurately recognizing and expressing their emotions, they find it really difficult to manage their behaviour. As children and young people develop an understanding of their internal body signals, they develop their understanding and awareness of their feelings and emotions. This enables them to express themselves more accurately and to connect with other people, build resilience and wellbeing. In addition, it is easier for kids to make and keep friends if they can understand and express their emotions. This is true for all people regardless of their age, stage of development, background and living situation.

2 MANAGING BEHAVIOUR CAN BE DIFFICULT FOR MANY CHILDREN

Many children, including those with disabilities and/or trauma of all ages seem to struggle with emotional regulation. They do not always exhibit typical emotional signals, which can make it hard for other people to help co-regulate them. Co-regulation is when someone helps someone to manage their emotions and feelings. For example, when an infant cries and they are fed, feeding them is a co-regulation strategy. Babies and infants require a lot of co-regulating. As children develop more awareness of and understanding of their emotions and feelings, they need less and less co-regulating and begin to be able to self-manage and self-regulate.

If you have a child with a disability, it is important to understand that difficult behaviour is NOT an inherent part of disability but where parents and educators do not know this, they can apply ineffective strategies. All children and young people, and even adults can be supported to develop the skills to recognize and express emotions appropriately.

There are three main reasons why children and young people can struggle with managing their feelings and emotions:

1. Disempowerment, Disenfranchisement, Trauma – both personally experienced and intergenerational (Shields, Cicchetti, & Ryan, 1994)
2. Mental health difficulties – anxiety and depression (Zamariola et al., 2019)
3. Developmental disabilities that have self-management & self-regulation difficulties (Gross and Thompson, 2007)

It is important to understand that between 25 and 50% (a quarter to a half) of children and young people will experience a mental health difficulty. Rates are higher for individuals with disability that those without. It is not inevitable that your child will develop a mental health difficulty, even if they have multiple disabilities. However, without a good understanding of their emotions and feelings, it is more likely.

The best protective factors for mental health are feeling valued, having a sense of belonging and having at least one-person care about you. This means that you as a parent or educator can be that one person who cares, and this can be invaluable.

Department of Health: Report on the second Australian Child and Adolescent Survey of Mental Health and Wellbeing (August 2015)

Overall prevalence of mental disorders in children and adolescents in Australia

Overall prevalence **13.9%**

16 – 24 year olds   75 – 85 year olds

Evaluation report of the *KidsMatter* primary mental health initiative in South Australian schools (Dicks, Shearer, Slee, and Butcher, 2010):

Prevalence of mental disorders with diagnosed disability

(a single diagnosed disability)   (more than one disability)

Children and young people with disability are more vulnerable to mental health difficulties due to **complex interrelationships between disability and other medical, social and psychological factors**

Helping Children Understand and Express Emotions

When your understanding of the world and sense of well-being vary from the majority culture and/or your value is portrayed as less than others, disempowerment or disenfranchisement can ensue. For children and young people from minority cultures, or with disabilities, they can feel as if they are valued less if they do not see themselves or people like them represented positively in books and on screens.

Sadly, when children and young people are not able to understand and express their emotions helpfully, they can be thought of as bad or naughty by other people, which can be very disempowering. Other people prefer people who can self-regulate their emotions. No-one wants to be around someone who yells and hits seemingly randomly.

Developing and improving interoception, leads to the ability to understand emotions, which can empower individuals to connect to self, to country and to others (personal discussions with Aboriginal Australians 2016-2019). Once you can connect to yourself and others, then you can make friendships and be seen for the individual you are, rather than being labelled as the 'naughty' or 'bad' child.

One of the reasons that children and young people can struggle with their emotions and feelings is biological. When anyone experiences a significant amount of stress or trauma, human biology creates a number of feedback loops that can increase the likelihood of behaviours that can appear challenging, or naughty or bad. "Chronic cumulative stressors also disrupt the self-regulatory processes that help children cope with external demands." (Evans & Kim, 2013).

Chronic stress also impacts the ability of children and young people to learn as it reduces the integration of new information into existing memories. (Vogel, & Schwabe, 2016). For this reason, if a child is not able to learn new skills or knowledge, it is important to consider their levels of stress. Using the strategies in this book will be useful to help decrease the biological impact of stress in the moment and over time.

Stress or distress, impact humans in a number of ways. A small amount of stress is important as it helps humans to learn, but too much is not good for us at all. Too much stress or trauma can lead to us not being able to tell the difference between life threatening events and other events, meaning that we go into survival mode when we don't need to. The human survival mode is housed in the most ancient part of the human brain. It is sometimes referred to as the reptile or ancient brain.

3 BEHAVIOUR, EMOTIONS AND THE BRAIN

It is important to understand how the brain impacts emotions and behaviour. One of the easiest ways to learn about this is using Dan Siegal's hand model of the brain.

In the hand model of the brain, the arm represents the spinal column and the wrist the brain stem. Whatever is touching the palm is what controls the brain. So, when the hand is open as in the picture below on the left, the survival brain is in control – which will result in fight/ flight/ freeze/ flop/ drop.

The brainstem controls some of our basic biological process such as breathing and heartbeat. The palm of our hand represents the ancient part of the brain – the reptile brain or survival brain, the thumb represents the emotional part of our brain and the fingers the thinking cap of the brain. The fingertips of the middle fingers represent the mindfulness and interoceptive awareness (conscious perception of internal body signals) parts of the brain.

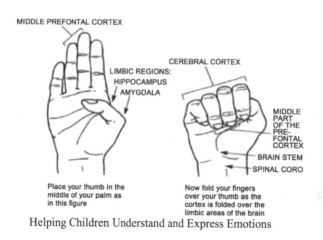

Helping Children Understand and Express Emotions

The hand model of the brain can be represented more accessibly for children and their parents or teachers by using cartoons character, emojis and a hat, superimposed onto the

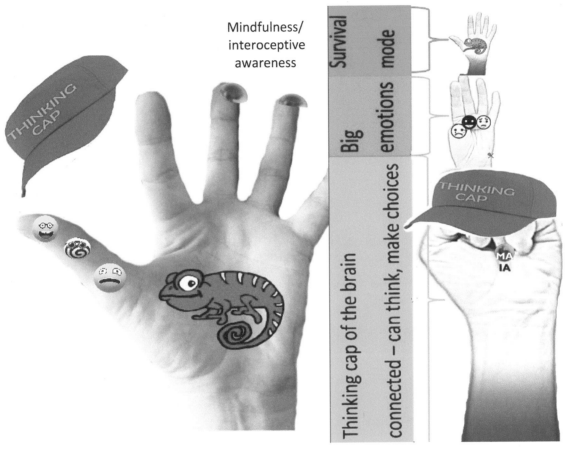

hand.

The thinking cap of the brain lifts up as we experience stress, as our sympathetic nervous system is activated. When our sympathetic nervous system is in overload, our survival brain takes over. Our sympathetic nervous system is one half of our autonomic nervous system, the other half being our parasympathetic nervous system. Our parasympathetic nervous system enables us to rest and digest when it is activated. These function sort of like a see-saw, as you can only be getting stressed or resting, you can't do both at the same time. The autonomic nervous system uses neuro-transmitters to increase or decrease activity on each side.

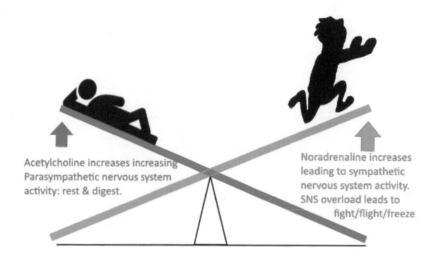

Acetylcholine increases increasing Parasympathetic nervous system activity: rest & digest.

Noradrenaline increases leading to sympathetic nervous system activity. SNS overload leads to fight/flight/freeze

Doing the activities in this book activates the parasympathetic nervous system, and brings the thinking cap of the brain back down, as the activities engage the mindfulness/interoceptive awareness part of the brain. This means that the activities biologically and neurologically calm the person doing them. It is always helpful to do the activities together, parent and child or teacher and whole class, as both calm and difficult emotions and feelings are contagious, which is why when one person is angry it can trigger anger in the people around.

If you have low interoceptive awareness you do NOT FEEL or EXPRESS 0-99

the build up of noradrenaline, which is the thinking cap of the brain starting to lift

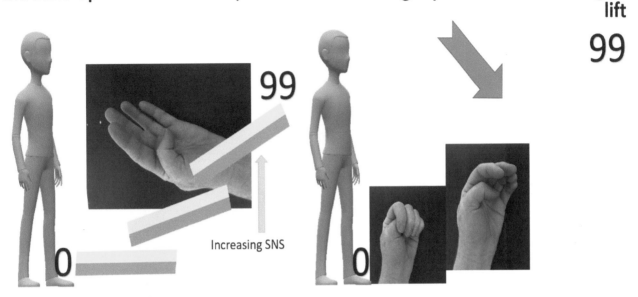

99

99 is big emotions and no clear thinking, 100 is SNS overload (survival instinct mode)and reptile brain takes over as you flip your lid/lose it.

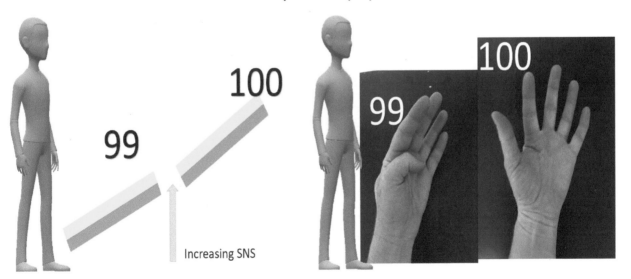

As we develop interoception we will start to feel our emotions BEFORE they are big.

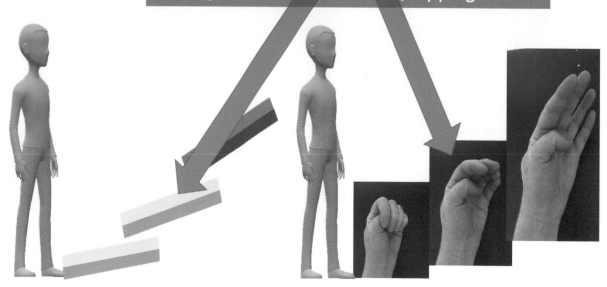

Which means we can do something about it, which prevents SNS overload/flipping our lid

The interoception center of the brain is the insula. We know from neuroscience research that in order to improve connections in our brain, to improve the functioning of any part of our brain, we need to use the connections repeatedly to hard wire or fix the new connections in. In other words, the activities in this book will develop or improve your interoception, but in order to ensure that your brain is able to keep that improvement in interoception, the activities or similar ones, needs to be repeated a large number of times over a period of 2-3 months.

Because trauma of any kind can 'turn down' our ability to feel our feelings and emotions, it is important that these activities are carried out in a safe space, when you are feeling ok. They are of no use during panic! This is because the survival brain is in control and there is no thinking going on, so any demand or request to do anything is likely to be interpreted as further danger by the reptile brain. If you are using these in a school, preschool or a residential setting, it is best to incorporate them into your day two or three times each day, so that they act as an emotional reset at typically difficult times of the day such as first thing in the morning, after breaks/recess and after lunch. Parents may want to do the activities first thing in the morning, after school pick up and before bed.

People who experience significant trauma will lose some of their interoceptive skills and will require more practice during times they are feeling safe, to restore their interoception. Interoceptive awareness is a pre-requisite for recognizing your emotions.

4 RECOGNIZING & UNDERSTANDING EMOTIONS & FEELINGS

It is easier than you might think to see if you or your child/student doesn't have a good ability to recognize and understand emotions and feelings. Feelings and emotions are a collection of body states. Think about when you have a *'funny feeling'* in your tummy. This could signal that you are unwell, or that you are about to vomit, or that you are nervous, or that you are in love, or that, if female, you are about to get your period.

The only way to know which of these it might be is to have another body signal. Even having an understanding of context will not be the total answer, as you may think the

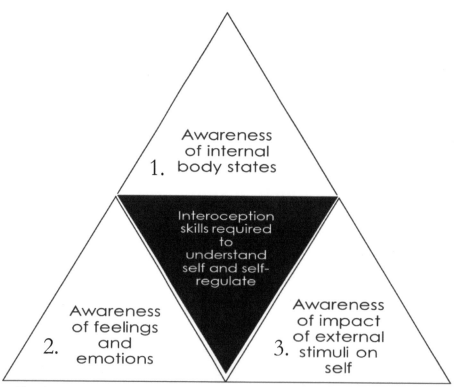

feeling is signally that you are in love but then you get vomiting and diarrhea!

1. Awareness of internal body states – this is the very base of interoceptive awareness, the conscious perception of internal body signals. If you don't know you have a heart-beat, you can't tell if it is beating fast or slow. A lack of this explains how people can break bones, have a stroke or be constipated and not know.

Interoceptive awareness is of any/all internal body signals e.g.:

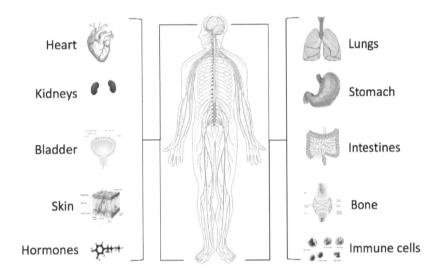

2. Awareness of feelings and emotions – once you have got a good range of interoceptive awareness then you can start to recognize and understand emotions. For example, I know I feel ill when my skin is clammy and I have a funny feeling in my tummy and my head feels dizzy. Feelings relate to our biological needs; hungry, need to go to the toilet, thirsty, tired etc. and emotions are social /relational. These are often represented by emoticons, but are actually felt/experienced differently by different

people. So, you will feel anger differently than other people in your family/school.

3.   Awareness of how things outside of you, impact you. For example, the temperature outside or in your room, impacts on your body temperature. If you don't notice being hot or cold, then you are unlikely to realize that your body is getting dangerously hot or cold. This is clearly seen in children who are dressed completely inappropriately for the weather and when asked, in the summer when dressed in a sweater; "aren't you hot?" and in the winter when in a t-shirt; "aren't you cold?", they say no. These are the wrong questions, as their body is hot/cold, but they are not able to feel it and so don't take the external temperature into account. A more effective way to communicate at this point would be; *

Summer, overheating child – "It is very hot out today and I can see that you are sweating. You need to take your sweater off or your body will overheat."

Winter, cold child – "It is very cold today and I can see that your fingers are going blue. You need to put a coat on or your body will get too cold."

*Some people have medical conditions which impact their thermoregulation and they may require a slightly higher/lower body temperature but in general humans require a core body temperature of approximately between 36.5–37.5 °C (97.7–99.5 °F).

So, using these three steps, in order to be able to self-regulate I need to be able to notice and understand my internal body signals, then understand how those body signals go together to represent my emotions and feelings and then understand how things outside of me impact me. As an example, I might start to notice my neck muscles and my head tension and then understand that when my head is tense and my neck muscles are sore that this is frustration. I then learn that my teacher can help me, which decreases my frustration, so I can ask them for help. I also learn that my brother increases my frustration, so when I notice my sore neck and tense head, I can walk away from my brother, to prevent my frustration increasing.

Understanding emotions and feelings is important if we are to connect to others and be able to have and express empathy and sympathy. A young lady that I was working with told me that she knew when she was getting sad *"because that water stuff runs down your face".* This is not what happens when you are 'getting' sad. It may happen when you are very sad, or when you are laughing so much that you cry. This young lady had no concept that being sad was an uncomfortable emotion.

It is important to be open with your children/students/clients about uncomfortable as well as pleasant emotions and feelings. For example, when I was teaching four-year olds in London, I would tell them when I was feeling angry or frustrated due to my trip into work; *"Good morning everyone. I am feeling grumpy today and am in a bad mood. This isn't your fault and I hope that I will be happier in a while."*

Too often adults hide their uncomfortable feelings, instead of modelling how to express and manage these feelings. If you personally don't understand your own emotions, or struggle to manage and express them safely, don't worry, the activities in this book will help you too. Children and adults who don't recognize or understand their feelings and emotions don't notice their emotions when they are emerging, and it is only when they are big emotions that they notice them, at which point everyone else does too! Also, at this point, the hand model of the brain shows us that there is no thinking happening, no ability to make conscious choices.

We can see this clearly in toddlers, who have not yet developed their interoception.

Often toddlers will refuse to go to bed when asked, even though they are tired, they don't recognize their tiredness. As they continue to stay up, they get more and more tired until they are overtired and they 'lose it'. Depending on their default 'survival behaviour' we will see a different behaviour. Those toddlers who are flopper/droppers will literally flop or drop to the floor, whereas those who are flight by default will toddle off as fast as they can. A toddler whose default is fight may yell and scream or hit and bite the nearest person. When in survival mode, the sympathetic nervous system is in overload, and there is no conscious thinking possible, so if approached, the child/adult can't process whether or not the person is coming to help or attack. This is why approaching someone in overload/survival mode is a bad idea and often ends up in being hurt by them.

Doing the activities in this book 2-3 times a day will, over a period of 8-10 weeks decrease the frequency of big emotions and increase the awareness of when emotions are getting too big to handle, before overload.

PNS dominant	Homeostasis	Slight SNS dominance	SNS dominant	SNS overload
Thinking cap of the brain connected – can think, make choices			Big emotions	Survival mode

THINKING CAP

MA
IA

5 ACTIVITIES

In order for these activities to develop or improve interoceptive awareness, they must be done together and done twice, with the following steps each time:

1. All do the activity which changes ONE aspect of the body.

2. Talk about or sign or point to where you each felt something different in your body from before and during the activity.

3. Decide and agree where you are going to focus on trying to feel something when you redo the activity. All redo the activity focusing on the body area/part that you decided on.

Interoception activities always focus on ONE change in body state as this enables the active noticing of internal body signals. The activities can focus on ONE of:

➢ Muscles

➢ Breathing

➢ Temperature

➢ Pulse

INTEROCEPTION STEPS

1. DO AN ACTIVITY THAT CHANGES ONE OF YOUR BODY STATES eg; breathing, muscles, temperature or pulse

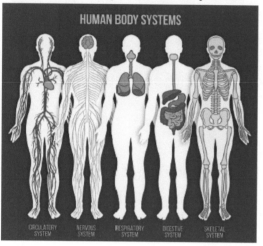

2. ASK YOURSELF: WHAT DO I NOTICE?

3. REPEAT ACTIVITY & FOCUS ON WHAT YOU NOTICE, FOR EXAMPLE THE SENSATION IN A PARTICULAR BODY PART

DOING INTEROCEPTION CREATES CONNECTIONS IN YOUR BRAIN

https://mindfulbodyawareness.com

Helping Children Understand and Express Emotions

It is important to understand that everyone is different and that anyone can have some areas of good interoception and some of poor interoception. Doing these activities strengthens the ability of the brain to notice and interpret the body signals that make up feelings and emotions, and to be calm enough to manage and express emotions.

Many of the thousands of children and young people who have been doing interoception activities in schools and preschools in South Australia have said that they find it easier to notice their muscle tension changes than any of the other body state changes. For this reason, I am presenting muscle activities first. However, it doesn't matter what order you do them in, or how frequently you do one versus another. If you/your child doesn't feel anything at all with one of the activities, that is an indication that you need to do that activity again. The more you/your child notice in terms of internal body signals the better the interoceptive awareness, which is the foundation for understanding and expressing emotions.

The following pages have some activities for each major part of the body in the muscles section, and a selection of breathing, temperature and pulse activities. If you would like to watch and join in with some interoception videos, have a look at the interoception activities section of my Healthy Possibilities YouTube Channel.

Channel: - https://www.youtube.com/channel/UCyIovxevV3W2l2WXHDBkKxA

Interoception activities playlist:

https://www.youtube.com/watch?v=MJEmgG4wxJk&list=PLXTC2Uqaw5-

3sO7rricA5pR2VChvT81oH

MUSCLES - HANDS STRETCH

These can be done sitting or standing or lying down, however you feel like doing them. These develop awareness of hand muscles.

1. Have your hands relaxed and then stretch them out as wide as possible

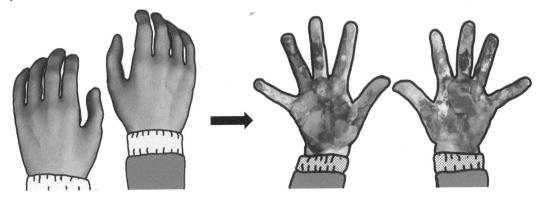

2. Talk about or sign or point to where you each felt something different in your body from before and during the activity.

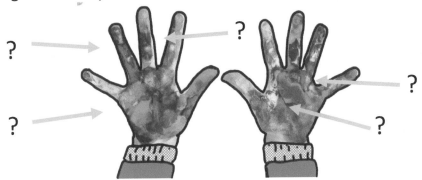

3. Decide and agree where you are going to focus on trying to feel something when you redo the activity.
e.g. Focus on; webbing between fingers, thumb, back of hand, sides of fingers.

4. All redo the activity focusing on the body area/part that you decided on.

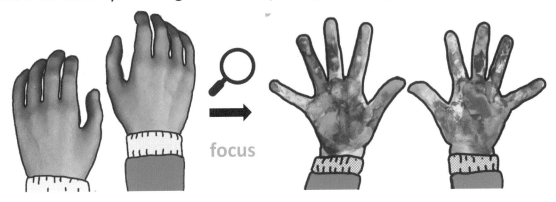

focus

Helping Children Understand and Express Emotions

MUSCLES - HANDS SQUISH

These can be done sitting or standing or lying down, however you feel like doing them. These develop awareness of hand muscles.

1. Have your hands relaxed and then stretch them out as wide as possible

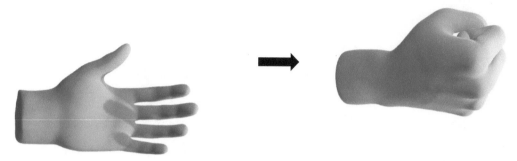

2. Talk about or sign or point to where you each felt something different in your body from before and during the activity.

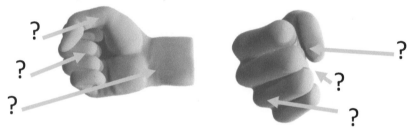

3. Decide and agree where you are going to focus on trying to feel something when you redo the activity.
e.g. Focus on; knuckles, palm, back of hand, side of little finger.

4. All redo the activity focusing on the body area/part that you decided on.

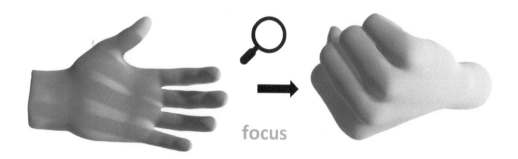

focus

MUSCLES - FEET STRETCH

These can be done sitting or standing or lying down, however you feel like doing them. These develop awareness of feet and toe muscles.

1. Have your feet relaxed and then stretch the toes as wide as possible

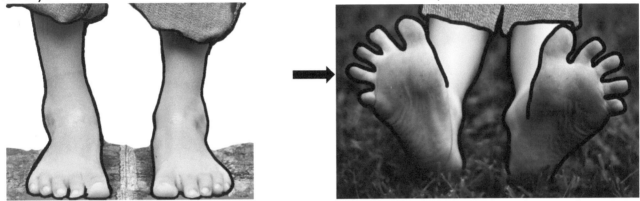

2. Talk about or sign or point to where you each felt something different in your body from before and during the activity.

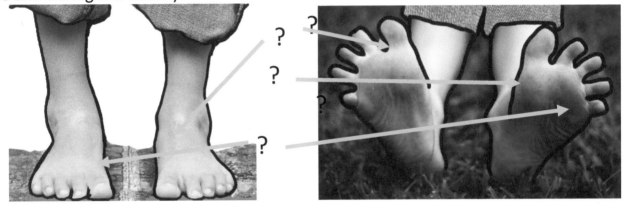

3. Decide and agree where you are going to focus on trying to feel something when you redo the activity.

e.g. Focus on; ball of the foot, big toes, arch of foot, outside of foot, arch

4. All redo the activity focusing on the body area/part that you decided on.

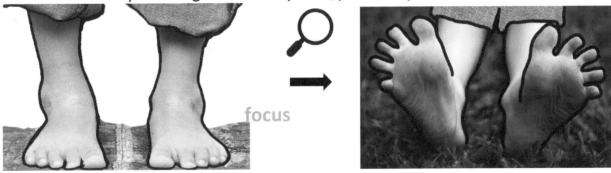

focus

Helping Children Understand and Express Emotions

MUSCLES - FEET SQUISH

These can be done sitting or standing or lying down, however you feel like doing them. These develop awareness of feet and toe muscles.

1. Have your feet relaxed and then stretch the toes as wide as possible

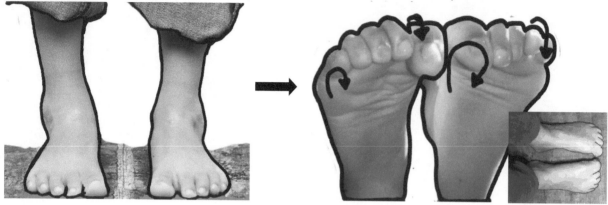

2. Talk about or sign or point to where you each felt something different in your body from before and during the activity.

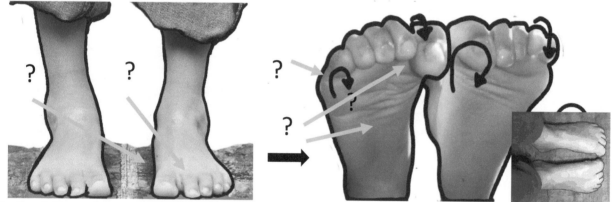

3. Decide and agree where you are going to focus on trying to feel something when you redo the activity. e.g. Focus on; ball of the foot, big toes, arch of foot, outside of foot, arch

4. All redo the activity focusing on the body area/part you decided on.

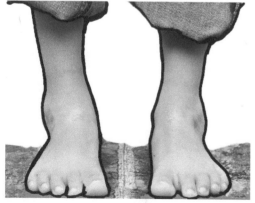 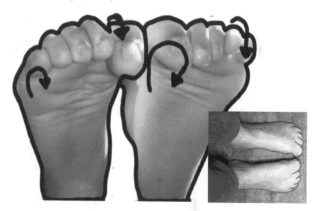

MUSCLES – SHOULDER/NECK TENSE-RELAX

These can be done sitting or standing. These develop awareness of shoulder and neck muscles; they may be felt in the back and pecs too.

1. Have your neck and shoulders relaxed and then pull your shoulders up, hold for 30 seconds then relax back.

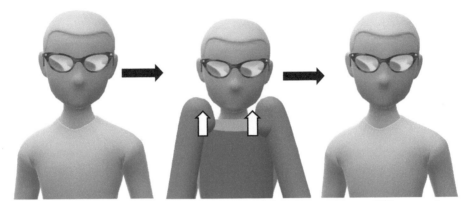

2. Talk about or sign or point to where you each felt something different in your body from before and during the activity.

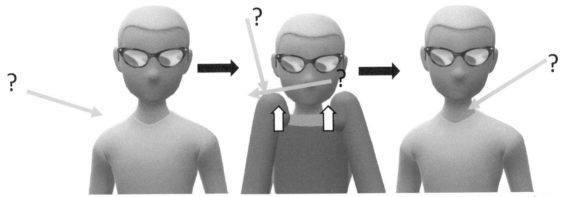

3. Decide and agree where you are going to focus on trying to feel something when you redo the activity. e.g. Focus on; sides or back of neck, top or front of shoulder joint, pecs

4. All redo the activity focusing on the body area/part you decided on.

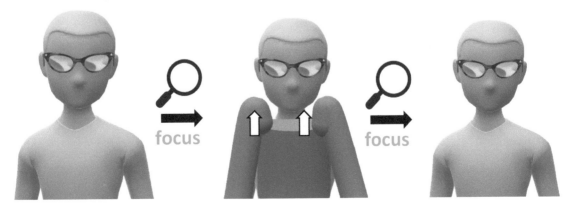

MUSCLES - CALF MUSCLES

These need to be done standing up. These develop awareness of calf muscles, they may be felt in the thighs, feet and hips too.

1. Standing up walk on the spot with your feet flat on the floor for a minute and then rise up onto your toes and walk on the spot on your tiptoes.

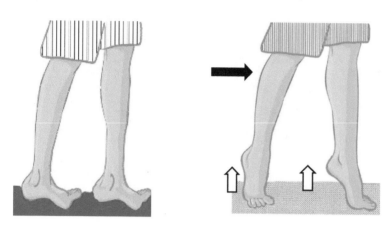

2. Talk about or sign or point to where you each felt something different in your body when you were walking flat on your feet versus when you were walking on your tiptoes.

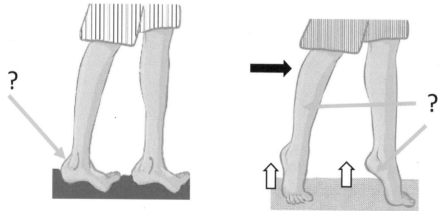

3. Decide and agree where you are going to focus on trying to feel something when you are walking on your tiptoes. e.g. Focus on; your calf muscles

4. All redo the activity focusing on the body area/part that you decided on.

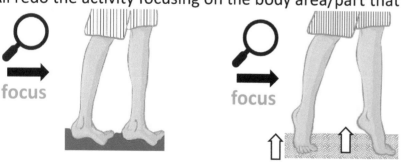

focus   focus

MUSCLES - LEG MUSCLES (SQUATS)

These can be done with your back against the wall. These develop awareness of muscles in the quads, glutes, and hamstrings and, they also may be felt in the calves too.

1. Stand with your back to the wall, then slowly lower your body down as you step your feet away, until you are positioned like the picture below. Hold this position as long as you feel comfortable doing so.

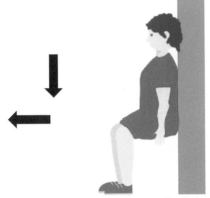

2. Talk about or sign or point to where you each felt your muscles when you were doing your wall squat.

3. Decide and agree where you are going to focus on trying to feel something when you do the wall squat. e.g. Focus on; your quad muscles.

4. All redo the activity focusing on the body area/part you decided on.

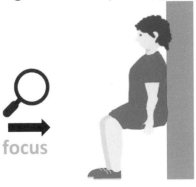

MUSCLES - ARM MUSCLES

These can be done standing up or sittings down. These develop awareness of muscles in the rotator cuff, and they also may be felt in the arms, shoulders and back.

1. Standing or sitting, put one arm across the front of your chest at shoulder height. Use your other arm to hold it in place for 30-60 seconds. The try doing this using the other arm.

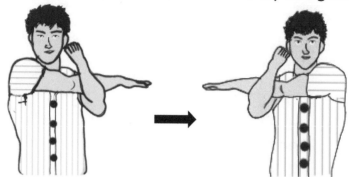

2. Talk about or sign or point to where you each felt your muscles when you were doing arm stretches.

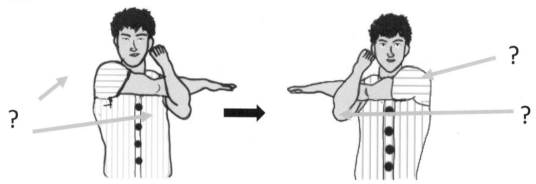

3. Decide and agree where you are going to focus on trying to feel something when you do the wall squat. e.g. Focus on; your rotator cuff.

4. All redo the activity focusing on the body area/part you decided on.

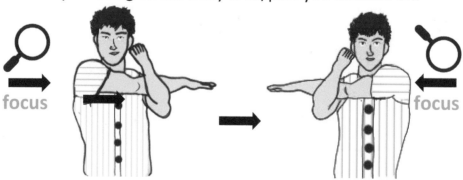

MUSCLES - CORE MUSCLES

These need to be done from sitting on the floor. These develop awareness of core muscles and they also may be felt in the legs, arms and back.

1. Sitting on the floor, place your feet flat on the floor and use your hands to support your balance. Then raise your legs up in the air, so your body forms a V.

2. Talk about or sign or point to where you each felt your muscles when you holding the V, versus sitting with your feet flat.

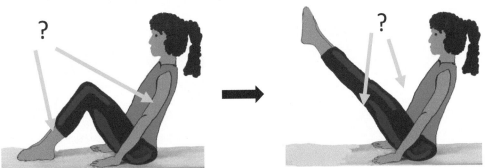

3. Decide and agree where you are going to focus on trying to feel something when you hold the V position. e.g. Focus on; your core muscles.

4. All redo the activity focusing on the body area/part you decided on.

Helping Children Understand and Express Emotions

BREATHING – BELLY BREATHING

1.Standing or sitting down, be still and put your hands on our belly, just below our diaphragm, this is behind your ribcage at the bottom of the ribs. Do this for 30-60 seconds.

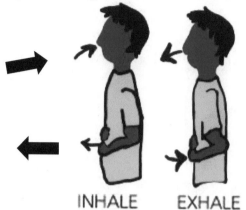

INHALE   EXHALE

2. Talk about or sign or indicate how far your belly extended when you breathed in, and how far it sank back in when you exhaled.

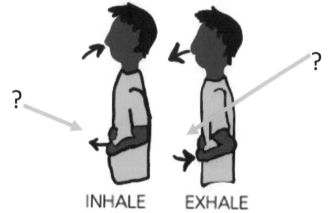

INHALE   EXHALE

3. Decide and agree where you are going to focus on trying to feel something when you do the belly breathing. e.g. Focus on; your belly rising and falling.

4. All redo the activity for 30-60 seconds focus on how your belly falls and rises.

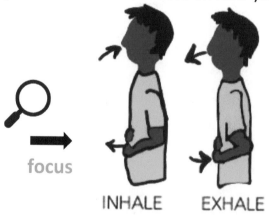

focus

INHALE   EXHALE

EQUALIZING BREATHING

1. Standing or sitting down, be still and start to breathe in through your nose and out through your mouth naturally. Then count up to four as you breathe in and count to four as you breathe out. Do this for 30-60 seconds.

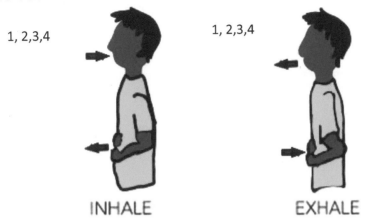

2. Talk about or sign or indicate when you can feel the breath on your face or your nostrils.

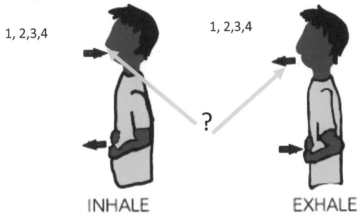

3. Decide and agree where you are going to focus on trying to feel something when you do the equalizing breathing. e.g. your nostrils.

All redo the activity focusing for 30-60 seconds on how the breath feels on your nostrils.

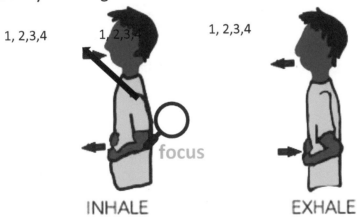

EXTENDED BREATHING

1. Standing or sitting down, be still and start to breathe in through your nose and out through your nose naturally. Then count up to four as you breathe in and count to six as you breathe out. Do this for 30-60 seconds.

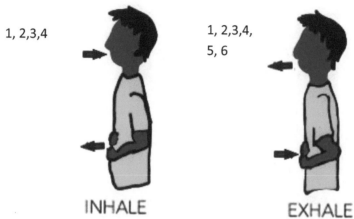

1, 2,3,4

1, 2,3,4, 5, 6

INHALE   EXHALE

2. Talk about or sign or indicate when you can feel a difference in your body. Is there someone that feels calmer?

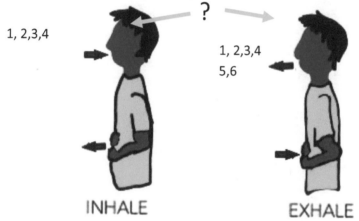

1, 2,3,4

?

1, 2,3,4 5,6

INHALE   EXHALE

3. Decide and agree where you are going to focus on trying to feel something when you do the extended breathing. e.g. Focus on; your head, does it feel clearer?
4. All redo the activity focusing on how the breath feels on your nostrils.

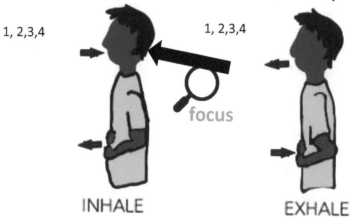

1, 2,3,4

1, 2,3,4

focus

INHALE   EXHALE

TEMPERATURE - COLD

1. Standing or sitting down, get a container of ice cubes and a container of tap water. Put your hands into the tap water and hold them there for 30-60 seconds. Then hold some of the ice cubes for as long as you feel comfortable, up to 15 seconds.

2. Talk about or sign or indicate which one is colder. How can you tell? Where can you feel the cold the most?

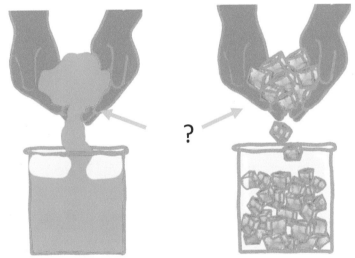

3. Decide and agree where you are going to focus on trying to feel the cold on your hand.

4. All redo the activity focusing on how your fingers feel in the ice.

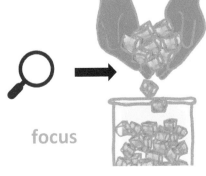

focus

TEMPERATURE - WARM

1. Standing or sitting down, rub your hands together fast for 30-60 seconds. Does this make your hands warmer or colder?

2. Talk about or sign or indicate whether your hands feel warmer or cooler? Which part of your hands feels the warmest?

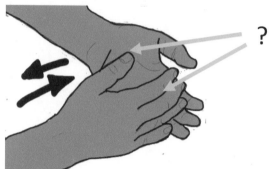

3. Decide and agree where you are going to focus on trying to feel the warm on your hand. E.g. focus on either your fingers or palms.

4. All redo the activity focusing on how warm you can make your palms.

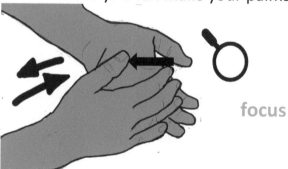

focus

PULSE

For some people using their pulse to monitor whether their body is in parasympathetic or sympathetic nervous system dominance can help to minimize the likelihood that they will go into sympathetic nervous system overload/survival mode. Everyone has a slightly different 'normal' for each and the quality/feel of the heart rate is a signal as well as the speed.

Normal Heart Rate by Age (beats/minute) Reference: PALS Guidelines, 2015 https://www.pedscases.com/pediatric-vital-signs-reference-chart		
Age	**Sleeping Rate** **PNS dominant – SNS dominance**	**Awake Rate** **Homeostasis – SNS dominant**
Infant (1 mo-1 y)	90-160	100 -190
Toddler (1-2 y)	80-120	98 -140
Preschool (3-5 y)	65-100	80 -120
School-age (6-11 y)	58-90	75 -118
Adolescent (12-15 y)	50-90	60 -100

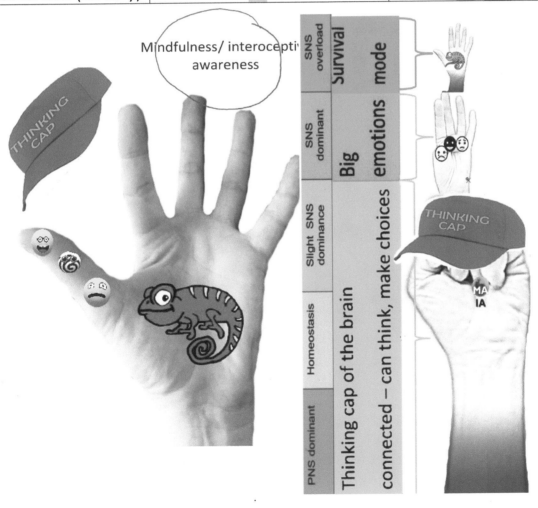

PULSE

ACTIVITY WITH SMART WATCH

You don't need to be able to read to use a smart watch as some of the more expensive ones will give you a graphic indicating your stress level. Cheaper smart watches that you might like to trial for yourself or someone else may just show the actual heart rate. The accuracy varies between watches, but it can be a useful indicator of whether you are getting calmer or less calm.

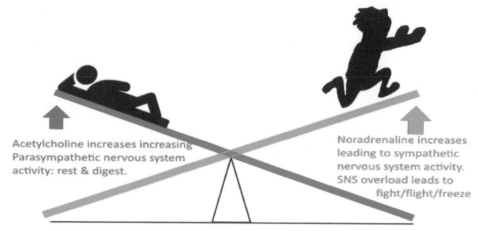

Acetylcholine increases increasing Parasympathetic nervous system activity: rest & digest.

Noradrenaline increases leading to sympathetic nervous system activity. SNS overload leads to fight/flight/freeze

Wearing a smart watch, take your pulse and then if able run on the spot for a minute. If this is not possible, then move any of your body parts as much as possible as quickly as possible for a minute. Then retake your pulse.

What did you notice?
What happens if you run on the spot for two minutes?
What changes did you notice in your body?

PULSE WITHOUT SMART WATCH

Some people find it very difficult or uncomfortable to take their own pulse, whilst others find it gives them a really good indication of how calm or not, they are. To take your pulse manually you use the first and second fingertips (never your thumb as it has its own pulse) and place them on one of your arteries, often the wrist or the neck. For this activity you can either focus on how the pulse feels under your fingertips OR you can count the pulses for 15 seconds. It is very difficult to count accurately for a minute so most people count for 15 seconds and either times by four or just compare the before exercise and after pulse rates.

If you cannot find your pulse straight away tilt your wrist slowly back and forward under your fingertips.

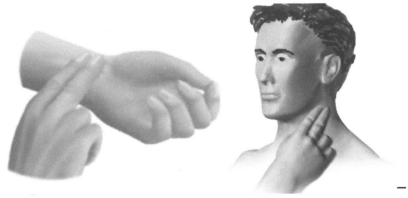

Take your pulse and then if able jump up and down for a minute. If this is not possible, then move any of your body parts as much as possible as quickly as possible for a minute. Then retake your pulse.

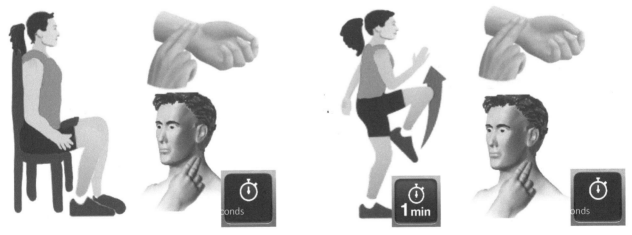

What did you notice?

What happens if you run on the spot for two minutes?

What changes did you notice in your body?

6 THE EVIDENCE BASE*

As a research field, neuroplasticity has challenged the prior belief that the human brain could not create new connections or neurons (neurogenesis) after very early childhood (Eriksson, Perfilieva, Björk-Eriksson, Alborn, Nordborg, Peterson, & Gage, 1998). The principal finding of research into neurogenesis and neuroplasticity is that the human brain can create new connections and in effect learn new skills throughout the lifespan, and that even significant damage to the brain can, with effective therapies, rewire itself to compensate or mitigate the damage. The brain's connectivity improves and structural changes can occur with new learning and that new learning can support structural changes designed to address individual challenges or difficulties. For example, improved functional connectivity between the posterior and anterior insula have also been observed following interventions (Farb, Anderson & Segal, 2013).

However, there is currently a lack of research literature investigating the implications for neuroplasticity in teaching and education systems, with Iuculano et al. (2015) being a notable exception. Iuculano et al. found that cognitive training for individuals with a diagnosed mathematical learning disability (MLD), in addition to improving individual mathematical skills, changed the structures of participants' brains, so that they were indistinguishable from their peers without mathematical learning difficulties, as illustrated in Figure 1 over the page.

*This section originally formed the basis of my confirmation for candidature (MSc) at the University of Queensland in 2019

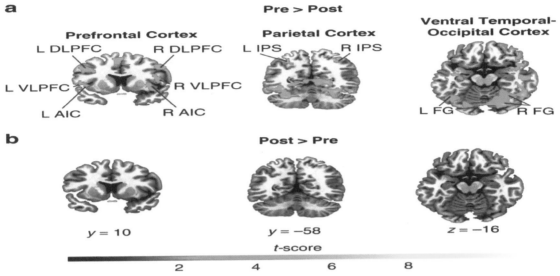

(a) Before tutoring, compared with post-tutoring, children with MLD (*n*=15) exhibited overactivation in several cortical areas in the Prefrontal Cortex, including the bilateral Dorsolateral and Ventrolateral Prefrontal Cortices (DLPFC and VLPFC), and the bilateral Anterior Insular Cortices (AIC); in the Parietal Cortex, encompassing the bilateral Intraparietal Sulci (IPS); and in the Ventral Temporal–Occipital Cortices, including the bilateral Fusiform Gyri (FG). (b) Post-tutoring, compared to pre-tutoring, no brain areas showed greater activation in children with MLD (*n*=15). Height threshold *P*<0.01, extent threshold *P*<0.01, significant by whole-brain voxel-wise paired-samples t-test.

Figure 1: Tutoring-induced functional brain plasticity in children with MLD. Iuculano et al. (2015) These brain scans illustrate the decrease in overactive areas of the brain in children with MLD, to levels typical of individuals without MLD, following the cognitive training.

Principles of neuroplasticity suggest that through feedback mechanisms within the brain, the representation of information selectively enables plastic changes that affect brain connections (Nahum, Lee, & Merzenich, 2013). For example, the events held in and attended to by working memory; selectively guide individuals to certain activities which sharpen and refine brain connections through learning (Ahissar, Nahum, Nelken, Hockstein, 2009). Neuroplasticity is "primarily expressed by a change in connectional strength at the synapse level, achieved both by increasing the powers and the numbers of synapses specifically supporting a progressively improving behaviour (Nahum, Lee, & Merzenich, 2013, p144). This idea is encapsulated in the iconic phrase "what fires together wires together", coined by Hebb (1949). These principles of neuroplasticity have also been implicated in teaching individuals with diagnoses of post-traumatic stress disorder to self-regulate behaviour (Mehling et al., 2018).

Behaviour, including self-regulation of behaviours and emotions are assumed to a product of brain systems, and thus can be changed through changing the brain systems according to neuroplasticity (Nahum, Lee, & Merzenich, 2013). This Masters' research is principally investigating how to effectively facilitate the development of self-regulation, using the concept of neuroplasticity, in students who are unable to manage their emotions and so exhibit behaviours that are challenging and/or harmful to themselves and/or others. Heatherton and Tice (1994) suggest that self-regulation refers to the individual's ability to control their own thoughts, emotions, and actions. Emotions and actions are understood to have a contextual element, in that individuals express emotions or carry out actions in response to their thoughts and/or their experience of the context around them (Wilutzky, 2015). Indeed, Grecucci, Koch, and Rumiati (2011) found that emotions can also impact imitative actions (for example if someone shouts loudly and excitedly, people around are more likely to shout loudly and excitedly back). Goleman (1995) described emotional and behavioural self-regulation as top level skills in an emotional intelligence hierarchy. Goleman suggested that emotional intelligence, sometimes known as social intelligence, is composed of three skill sets; emotional skills, cognitive skills, and behaviour skills. When these theories are looked at in conjunction with metacognition; thinking about thinking (Moses & Baird, 1999, Wellman, 1985) the key role of interoception can be identified.

Interoception is sometimes referred to as somatic awareness, and colloquially known as the eighth sense with the other seven being; sight, hearing, taste, smell, touch, proprioception, and vestibular (Lynch & Simpson, 2004). While most people are familiar with sight, hearing, taste, smell, touch, the vestibular and proprioception senses are focused on the awareness of the whole body. Vestibular refers to our sense of balance, which is governed by the inner ear and proprioception refers to the sense of where our body is placed in space, for example where our head ends and space starts, which is useful to prevent us banging our heads on overhanging objects.

Much like the other senses, interoception has two components; interoceptive awareness and interoceptive accuracy (Calì, Ambrosini, Picconi, & Mehling, 2015). Interoception can also be described as mindful body awareness, as it is the conscious perception (mindful) of internal body signals (body awareness). Mindfulness is a broad term, used in popular culture in a variety of ways. As a lifestyle concept mindfulness means to pay attention on purpose, in the present moment, and nonjudgmentally, whereas as a spiritual concept mindfulness can be used to mean being present and aware. In this proposal, mindful body awareness rather than mindfulness, is the focus. Mindful *body awareness* is taken as purposeful attention in the present moment *focused on changes and sensations within the body or self.* This focused attention should guide the plasticity of the brain to create and strengthen interoceptive awareness brain connections, as per the findings of Ahissar et al. (2009) that attention and working memory can drive neuroplasticity. Someone who is skilled at mindful body awareness, can for example, tell when their heart beat is signaling fear versus excitement because they can notice and recognize or identify all the other internal bodily signals that they are experiencing which help them to process and respond to their overall emotional state. On a more basic level, interoception enables people to know when they are hungry, thirsty, tired etc., all of which are necessary precursors to positive development and self-regulation.

Without interoception, it is probable that children and young people will be unable to develop metacognitive emotional abilities (Goodall, 2016). In general, it is evident that there is a huge variance in socio-emotional self-regulation, for example children who have experienced poverty and/or chronic stress are known to have attenuated self-regulation (Ryan & Kim (2013)). The other cohort with known reduction in self-regulation are those with mental illnesses. In mental illness, people respond atypically to internal and external stimuli. Zamariola, Frost, Van Oost, Corneille, & Luminet, (2019) in talking about people with depression, stated that "people with low interoceptive abilities show more difficulties in verbalizing their feelings and in decreasing the impact of emotions generated by negative experiences in daily life" (p. 480).

The links between increasing level of metacognition and emotional intelligence skills, highlight that the skill of self-assessing cognitive process is used to direct personal behaviour, which equates with both emotional and behavioural self-regulation which is the highest skill in interoception. The parallels between the levels of metacognition and interoception, where both start with knowing and noticing mental states then end with self-regulation illustrate the complexity of self-regulation. Mehling et al.'s (2018) research in war veterans with diagnosed PTSD, who were struggling to appropriately self-regulate, found that a 12-week integrative exercise program using aerobic and resistance exercise with mindfulness-based principles and yoga significantly improved mindfulness, interoceptive awareness, positive states of mind, and self-regulation. The research posited that integrative exercise conceptualized a holistic approach that directly aimed to improve interoceptive awareness. The rationale for improving interoceptive awareness was the idea that this would lead to improved interoceptive processing, which is known to be altered in individuals with PTSD (Lanius, Frewen, Tursich, Jetly, & McKinnon, 2015; Nicholson et al., 2016; Simmons, Strigo, Matthews, Paulus, & Stein, 2015).

Gross and Thompson (2007) proposed a model of emotion regulation in which people rely upon the constant cognitive reappraisal of emotional state to modulate early emotional response tendencies, before these emotions become extreme and lead to more extreme emotional responses or expression. Theoretically, self-regulation should be able to be improved in individuals using a principle of neuroplasticity, of using directed attention to create and strengthen brain connections during activities that direct attention to internal body states (mindful body awareness or interoception). As the individuals improve their interoception and are therefore able to cognitively appraise and reappraise their emotional states, leading to improved ability to self-regulate. This may mean that young people with trauma or intergenerational trauma who frequently exhibit low levels of self-regulation, may be able to develop higher levels of self-regulation following focused interventions. Yehuda et al. (2016) showed that preconception parental trauma was associated with epigenetic alterations in both the exposed parent and their children. They found "an intergenerational epigenetic priming of the physiological response to stress in offspring of highly traumatized individuals" (p. 379). In the context of Aboriginal peoples, Canadian research has highlighted the complex contexts that contribute to the intergenerational transmission of trauma in Aboriginal/First Nations people (Aguiar & Halseth, 2015). Nathan (2015, p. 371) writes about the "hurting hearts that are endemic in the post-colonial trauma" of Aboriginal Australians. Hurting hearts is a concept that may not resonate with behaviour coaches or teachers as a possible cause of difficulties with self-regulation, but sits well with understandings of Māori (*Te Whare Tapa Whā*) and Pacific Island models of health and wellbeing which are more holistic than dominant culture models of health and/or wellbeing in Australia. These models provide a framework for understanding the relationship between context and well-being, including emotional health. Emotional health is based on the ability to recognize and manage your emotions.

Figure 2 Māori Health Model, Durie (n.d)   Pasifika Health Model, Pulotu-Endemann

(2007)

The Māori model includes; wairua (spirit or spiritual), the role of the whānau (family) and the balance of the hinengaro (mind) as well as the tinana (body or physical manifestations of illness). Pulotu-Endemann's (2007) Pacific model includes even more domains that show the cultural links between health and wellbeing in ways that more closely reflect Aboriginal Australian cultures.

If well-being is understood as positive psychosocial functioning, then self-regulation is an antecedent to well-being (Balzarotti, Biassoni, Villani, Prunas, & Velotti, 2016), that in the above models fits into and impacts; relationships/family, spiritual, physical, and mental health. Due to the paucity of research about the role of poor or atypical interoceptive awareness in self-regulation, it has not been possible to confirm the role of interoception in difficulties in self-regulation or the presentation of challenging behaviour. A library search for "interoception" and "self-regulation" in the title, only found two journal articles (Gannon, 1977, Weiss et al., 2014) and a book (Mahler, 2015). Mahler (2015) posited that interoception was a key skill in developing the ability to self-manage in areas of toileting etc. that occupational therapists focus on for children on the autism spectrum. Weiss et al. (2014) was only concerned with the link between interoception and pain perception and not a wider emotional regulation. This gap in the literature is surprising as Füstös et al., in 2012 stated that "one prerequisite of successful emotion regulation is the awareness of emotional states, which in turn is associated with the awareness of bodily signals [interoceptive awareness (IA)] (p. 911).

Current observations of children and young people with complex needs indicated a lack of recognition of their own emotional states or feelings, until and unless these feelings and/or were extreme. These observations and follow up conversations indicated poor interoceptive awareness in these children and young people (Goodall, 2019). For example, not seeming to notice they were angry until they were enraged, nor noticing thirst until they were dehydrated. This lack of connection to self could be explained by either poor interoceptive accuracy or more likely poor interoceptive awareness. The link between interoceptive awareness and mindfulness, in relation to sense of self, can be found in research on the embodied sense of self (Cook-Cottone, 2015; Craig, 2003, 2008; Domasio, 1999).

Domasio (1999) proposed that human awareness of and experience of emotional feelings are reliant on neural states that represent internal body signals, with collections of body signals evoking feeling states/emotions that influence both cognition and behaviour.

If, for example, individuals were not noticing their emotional states, this would be why they didn't do anything about it, and once they were aware, it was too late to do anything about it as they were in sympathetic nervous system overload/survival mode (Goodall, 2019).

In Figure 3, the theoretical link between emotional arousal, state of the autonomic nervous system and Siegal's (2010) hand model of the brain are shown. In Siegal's model, the middle finger nail represents the mindfulness part of the brain, which can only be engaged when the fist is fully closed and the 'thinking cap of the brain' is engaged. As interoceptive awareness is the conscious perception of internal body signals, this model equates it with mindful body awareness (Goodall, 2016). Theoretically, engaging in mindful body awareness (interoception) activities will engage the mindfulness part of the brain, leading to the thinking cap of the brain also being engaged and the parasympathetic nervous system being activated, which would enable self-regulation. When individuals are in sympathetic nervous system overload, otherwise known as survival mode, they cannot self-regulate their emotions as the brain's survival instinct takes over (Siegal, 2010). In Figure 3, this is visually represented, so where students are unable to control their behaviours or regulate their emotions in the panic zone, as their survival instinct has overtaken conscious thought, resulting in behaviours that can be challenging to themselves and/or others. Interoception enables people self-regulate as they know when they are heading towards panic zone, enabling them to do something to prevent themselves entering panic zone.

Figure 3: Zones of regulation and understanding behaviour Department for Education (2019, p.3)

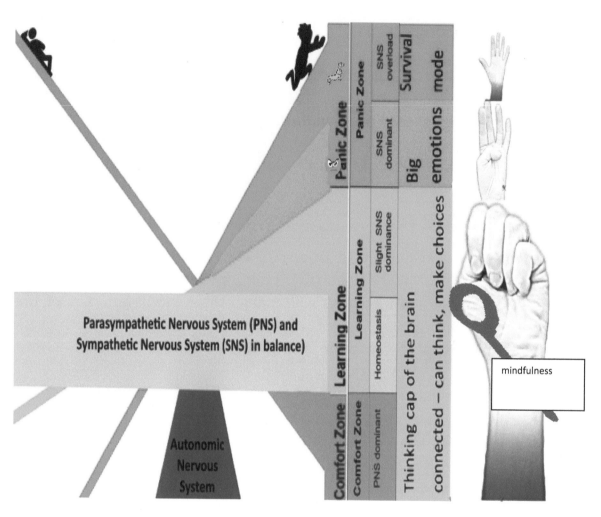

Mindfulness is known to lead to improvement for people with disabilities in relation to their experience of depression and anxiety, as well as improving self-compassion and compassion for others (Idusohan-Moizer, Sawicka, Dendle, & Albany, 2015). In a pilot study, researchers from the Center for Investigating Healthy Minds (CIHM) at the Waisman Center, University of Wisconsin-Madison taught teachers and children and young people in the Madison Metropolitan School District mindfulness. Flook et al., (2015) reported that children and young people in the research group said they felt more in control and responsible for their actions. Their teachers suggested that the children and young people in this mindfulness training research made fewer errors whilst demonstrating improved use of strategy in problem solving tasks involving working memory and improved emotion regulation. The CIHM also looked at preschools and teaching kindness and compassion through mindfulness and found that these children and young people showed greater improvements in social competence as well as higher levels of learning, health, and social-emotional development, whereas the control group exhibited more selfish behaviour over time (Flock et al., 2015). This suggests that it may be possible to teach emotional and behavioural self-regulation through mindful body awareness/interoception activities.

Interoceptive awareness can be broadly defined as the conscious perception of an internal bodily state, for example, one's heart beating and breathing. This definition can also apply to the mindful body awareness, the conscious noticing in the present moment of body signals. These senses are related to emotional experiences. Awareness of physiological internal body cues is altered in individuals who are affected by trauma, including intergenerational trauma, and neurodevelopmental disabilities including autism (Mahler, 2016; Schauder, Mash, Bryant, & Cascio, 2015). Against a background of the human species' survival instinct, including our biological need for and drive towards homeostasis, interoceptive awareness can be broadly split into three categories. These categories are; ability to notice internal body signals (Craig, 2002), ability to notice and interpret collections of body signals as emotions and feelings (Craig, 2009), and the ability to notice external signals and interpret the impact these will have on the body (Craig, 2009). Figure 4 depicts how the combination of these categories of interoceptive awareness enables people to respond to these signals, in effect, understand themselves, self-regulate and self-manage (Craig, 2007).

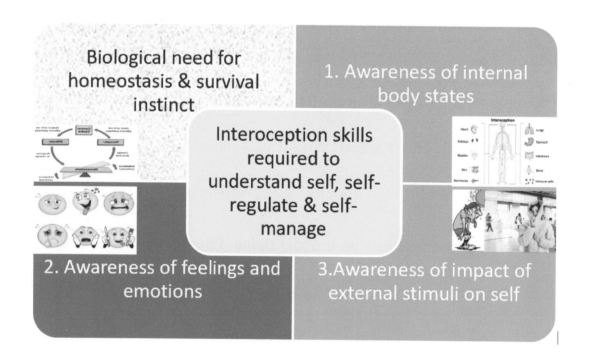

Figure 4: Aspects of interoceptive awareness (Goodall, 2019)

Füstös et al. (2012) suggested that self-regulation of emotions is reliant on both attention to and awareness of one's emotional state, which could be linked to, or interpreted as interoception. Self-regulation is commonly understood in education settings as the moderation or control of emotions and behaviour in order to follow social norms in context. This is sometimes referred to as self-control. Self-management on the other hand is related to the control of, or actioning of behaviours in order to fulfil biological needs, usually in accordance with a drive to return to homeostasis (Craig, 2007). Self-management behaviours include; drinking water when thirsty or putting a sweater on when cold. Self-management is more obviously linked to homeostasis, as evidenced by the need for our bodies to be within a particular temperature range, have energy input through food and output through waste elimination and energy usage, by muscle movement etc..

Interoception skills are required for a range of basic and more advanced functions such as knowing when to go to the toilet, being aware that you are becoming angry or upset, and being able to manage your emotions proactively. Children and young people who have not yet developed interoception skills struggle with not only their own emotions (Brewer & Bird, 2016), but with social interactions and just being around others (Goodall et al., 2019). There is a significant gap in the literature in the relationship between interoception and emotional regulation, with research only looking at how interventions involving interoception were effective in ameliorating a range of mental health disorders'

symptoms, (Khoury, Lutz, & Schuman-Olivier, 2018). Furman et al. (2013) found that

altered interoception in adults with major depression impacted the participants' ability to

feel positive as well as their ability to make decisions based on interoceptive signals.

However, there is a dearth of research on the impact of altered interoception on

developing or improving interpersonal difficulties, self-regulation, social anxiety or other

behaviours in adults or children. It seems likely that children and young people with well-

developed interoception are able to use both logic and emotions to respond to their

environment, whereas those without tend to rely solely on logic and have to carefully

think through their possible responses to each situation. Thinking through each situation

long term can be extremely tiring and can contribute to overload, shutdown, meltdowns,

anxiety, and depression

REFERENCES

Aguiar, W., & Halseth, R. (2015). *Aboriginal peoples and historic trauma: the processes of intergenerational transmission*. National Collaborating Centre for Aboriginal Health= Centre de collaboration nationale de la santé autochtone.

Birt, L., Scott, S., Cavers, D., Campbell, C., & Walter, F. (2016). Member Checking: A Tool to Enhance Trustworthiness or Merely a Nod to Validation? *Qualitative Health Research,* 26(13) 1802 –1811 https//doi.org/10.1177/1049732316654870

Brewer, R., Cook, R., & Bird, G. (2016). Alexithymia: A general deficit of interoception. *Royal Society Open Science*, 3(10). https://doi.org/10.1098/rsos.150664

Brown, K., Ryan, R., & Creswell, J. (2007). Mindfulness: Theoretical Foundations and Evidence for its Salutary Effects.*Psychological Inquiry, 18*(4), 211-237.

Calì, G., Ambrosini, E., Picconi, L., & Mehling, W. (2015). Frontiers | Investigating the relationship between interoceptive accuracy, interoceptive awareness, and emotional susceptibility | Psychology. Retrieved 23 July 2019, from https://www.frontiersin.org/articles/10.3389/fpsyg.2015.01202/full

Clarke, V., & Braun, V. (2013). Teaching thematic analysis: Overcoming challenges and developing strategies for effective learning. *The psychologist, 26*(2), 120-123. https://doi.org/10.1037/13620-004

Cook-Cottone, C. P. (2015). *Mindfulness and yoga for self-regulation: A primer for mental health professionals*. Springer Publishing Company. ProQuest Ebook Central, http://ebookcentral.proquest.com/lib/usq/detail.action?docID=2166654. Created from usq on 2019-07-11 05:51:10.

Craig, A. D. (2002). How do you feel? Interoception: The sense of the physiological condition of the body. *Nature Reviews Neuroscience, 3*(8), 655–666. https://doi.org/10.1038/nrn894

Craig, A. D. (2003). Interoception: the sense of the physiological condition of the body. *Current opinion in neurobiology, 13*(4), 500-505. https://doi.org/10.1016/S0959-4388(03)00090-4

Craig, A. D. (2007). Interoception and emotion: a neuroanatomical perspective. In: Lewis M, Haviland-Jones JM, Feldman Barrett L, editors. Handbook of emotions.

New York: Guilford Press. pp. 272–290.

Craig, A. D., & Craig, A. D. B. (2009). How do you feel--now? The anterior insula and human awareness. *Nature Reviews Neuroscience, 10*(1), 59–70. https://doi.org/10.1038/nrn2555

Creamer, E. G. (2017). *An introduction to fully integrated mixed methods research.* SAGE Publications.

Department for Education (2019) *Ready to Learn Interoception Kit.* Adelaide: Department for Education.

Department for Education, Regulation scale - HSP432. Adelaide: Department for Education.

Duckworth, A. L., & Carlson, S. M. (2013). Self-regulation and school success. *Self-regulation and autonomy: Social and developmental dimensions of human conduct, 40,* 208.

Durie, M. (n.d) *Te Whare Tapa Whā, Maori health model.* Ministry of Health – Manatū Hauora. Retrieved from https://www.health.govt.nz/our-work/populations/maori-health/maori-health-models/maori-health-models-te-whare-tapa-wha

Eriksson, P. S., Perfilieva, E., Björk-Eriksson, T., Alborn, A.-M., Nordborg, C., Peterson, D. A., & Gage, F. H. (1998). Neurogenesis in the adult human hippocampus. *Nature Medicine, 4*(11), 1313. https://doi.org/10.1038/3305

Evans, G. W., & Kim, P. (2013). Childhood poverty, chronic stress, self-regulation, and coping. *Child development perspectives, 7*(1), 43-48.

Farb, N. A., Anderson, A. K., & Segal, Z. V. (2012). The mindful brain and emotion regulation in mood disorders. *Canadian Journal of Psychiatry. Revue Canadienne de Psychiatrie, 57*(2), 70–77. https://doi.org/10.1177/070674371205700203

Flook, L., Goldberg, S.B., Pinger, L.J., & Davidson, R. J. (2015). Promoting prosocial behavior and self-regulatory skills in preschool children through a mindfulness-based kindness curriculum. *Developmental Psychology,* 51(1), 44–51. PMCID: PMC4485612 http://centerhealthyminds.org/assets/files-publications/FlookPromotingDevPsych.pdf

Furman, D. J., Waugh, C. E., Bhattacharjee, K., Thompson, R. J., & Gotlib, I. H. (n.d.). Interoceptive awareness, positive affect, and decision making in Major Depressive Disorder. *Journal of Affective Disorders, 151*(2), 780–785. Retrieved from https://www.academia.edu/30715453/Interoceptive_awareness_positive_affect

Füstös, J., Gramann, K., Herbert, B. M., & Pollatos, O. (2012). On the embodiment of emotion regulation: interoceptive awareness facilitates reappraisal. *Social cognitive and affective neuroscience, 8*(8), 911-917. https://doi-org.ezproxy.usq.edu.au/10.1093/scan/nss089

Gannon, L. (1977). The role of interoception in learned visceral control. *Biofeedback and Self-Regulation, 2*(4), 337–347. https://doi.org/10.1007/BF00998621

Goleman, D. (1995). *Emotional Intelligence: Why it can matter more than IQ.* New York: Bantam Books.

Goodall, E. (2016). Interoception 101 Activity Guide, Department for Education, South Australia

Grecucci, A., Koch, I., & Rumiati, R. I. (2011). The role of emotional context in facilitating imitative actions. *Acta Psychologica, 138*(2), 311–315. https://doi.org/10.1016/j.actpsy.2011.07.005

Gross, J.J., Thompson, R.A. (2007). Emotion regulation: conceptual foundations. In: Gross, J.J., editor. Handbook of Emotion Regulation. New York: Guliford, pp. 3–24.

Hebb, D.O. (1949). The Organization of Behavior. New York: J Wiley.

Heatherton, T. F., & Tice, D. M. (1994). *Losing control: How and why people fail at self-regulation.* San Diego, CA: Academic Press.

Idusohan-Moizer, H., Sawicka, A., Dendle, J., & Albany, M. (2015). Mindfulness-Based Cognitive Therapy for Adults with Intellectual Disabilities: An Evaluation of the Effectiveness of Mindfulness in Reducing Symptoms of Depression and Anxiety. *Journal of Intellectual Disability Research, 59*(2), 93-104.

Iuculano, T., Rosenberg-Lee, M., Richardson, J., Tenison, C., Fuchs, L., Supekar, K., & Menon, V. (2015). Cognitive tutoring induces widespread neuroplasticity and remediates brain function in children with mathematical learning disabilities. *Nature communications, 6,* 8453.

Khoury, N. M., Lutz, J., & Schuman-Olivier, Z. (2018). Interoception in Psychiatric Disorders: A Review of Randomized, Controlled Trials with Interoception-Based Interventions, *Harvard Review of Psychiatry, 26*(5), 250–263. https://doi.org/10.1097/HRP.0000000000000170

Lanius, R. A., Frewen, P. A., Tursich, M., Jetly, R., & McKinnon, M. C. (2015). Restoring large-scale brain networks in PTSD and related disorders: A proposal for neuroscientifically-informed treatment interventions. *E Psychotraumatol*, 6, 27313. https://doi.org/10.3402/ejpt.v6.27313

Lewis, M., Haviland-Jones, Jeannette M, & Barrett, Lisa Feldman. (2008). *Handbook of emotions* (3rd ed.). New York: Guilford Press.

Lynch, S. A., & Simpson, C. G. (2004). Sensory processing: Meeting individual needs using the seven senses. *Young Exceptional Children*, 7(4), 2-9. .

Mahler, K., (2015). *Interoception: The eighth sensory system.* KS: AAPC.

McCrudden, M. T., Marchand, G., & Schutz, P. (2019). Mixed methods in educational psychology inquiry. *Contemporary Educational Psychology*, 57, 1–8. https://doi.org/10.1016/j.cedpsych.2019.01.008

Mehling, W. E., Chesney, M. A., Metzler, T. J., Goldstein, L. A., Maguen, S., Geronimo, C., Neylan, T. C. (2018). A 12-week integrative exercise program improves self-reported mindfulness and interoceptive awareness in war veterans with posttraumatic stress symptoms. *Journal of Clinical Psychology*, 74(4), 554–565. https://doi.org/10.1002/jclp.22549

Morrow, S. L. (2005). Quality and trustworthiness in qualitative research in counseling psychology. *Journal of counseling psychology*, 52(2), 250. https://doi.org/10.1037/0022-0167.52.2.250

Moses, L.J. & Baird, J.A., (1999). Metacognition. In Wilson, R.A., & Keil, F.C. (Eds.). *The MIT encyclopaedia of the cognitive sciences* (pp. 533-535). Cambridge, MA:MIT Press.

Nahum, M., Lee, H., & Merzenich, M. M. (2013). Chapter 6—Principles of Neuroplasticity-Based Rehabilitation. In M. M. Merzenich, M. Nahum, & T. M. Van Vleet (Eds.), *Progress in Brain Research* (pp. 141–171). https://doi.org/10.1016/B978-0-444-63327-9.00009-6

Nathan, P. (2019). Creating a safe supportive environment (CASSE): a psychodynamically-informed community intervention for Aboriginal communities in Central Australia. In *Contemporary Psychodynamic Psychotherapy* (pp. 361-372). Academic Press. https://doi.org/10.1016/B978-0-12-813373-6.00025-8

Nicholson, A. A., Sapru, I., Densmore, M., Frewen, P. A., Neufeld, R.W., Theberge, J., Lanius, R. A. (2016). Unique insula subregion resting-state functional connectivity with amygdala complexes in posttraumatic stress disorder and its dissociative subtype. *Psychiatry Res*, *250*, 61–72. https://doi.org/10.1016/j.pscychresns.2016.02.002

Pulotu-Endemann, F.K. (2007). *A Pacific Model of Health: The Fonofale Model.* . Ministry of Health – Manatū Hauora. Retrieved from http://apps.centralpho.org.nz/Permalink/MoM/General%20Documents/MoM/Published/Pacific%20Health%20Forms/Fonofale%20model.pdf

Schauder, Mash, Bryant, & Cascio. (2015). Interoceptive ability and body awareness in autism spectrum disorder. *Journal of Experimental Child Psychology, 131*, 193-200.

Siegel, D. J. (2010). Mindsight: *The new science of personal transformation.* New York, Bantam Dell Publishing.

Simmons, A., Strigo, I. A., Matthews, S. C., Paulus, M. P., & Stein, M. B. (2009). Initial evidence of a failure to activate right anterior insula during affective set shifting in posttraumatic stress disorder. *Psychosom Med*, 71(4), 373–377. https://doi.org/10.1097/PSY.0b013e3181a56ed8

Sousa, B. J., & Clark, A. M. (2018). Sharing Diverse Voices: An Imperative for Qualitative Research. *International Journal of Qualitative Methods*, 17, 1–2. https://doi-org.ezproxy.usq.edu.au/10.1177/1609406918822012

Tashakkori, A., & Creswell, J. W. (2007). The new era of mixed methods. *Journal of Mixed Methods Research*, 1, 3-7. https://doi.org/10.1177/2345678906293042

Weiss, S., Sack, M., Henningsen, P., & Pollatos, O. (2014). On the interaction of self-regulation, interoception and pain perception. *Psychopathology, 47*(6), 377-382.

Wellman, H.M., (1985). The child's theory of mind: The development of conceptions of cognition. In Yussen, S.R., (Ed.) *The growth of reflection in children* (pp 169-206) New York: Academic.

Yehuda, R., Daskalakis, N. P., Bierer, L. M., Bader, H. N., Klengel, T., Holsboer, F., & Binder, E. B. (2016). Holocaust Exposure Induced Intergenerational Effects on FKBP5 Methylation. *Biological Psychiatry, 80*(5), 372–380. https://doi.org/10.1016/j.biopsych.2015.08.005Yoris, A., Esteves, S., Couto, B., Melloni, M., Kichic, R., Cetkovich, M. Sedeño, L. (2015). The roles of interoceptive sensitivity and metacognitive interoception in panic. *Behavioral and Brain Function: BBF, 11*, 14.

Zamariola, G., Frost, N., Van Oost, A., Corneille, O., & Luminet, O. (2019). Relationship between interoception and emotion regulation: New evidence from mixed methods. (Report). *Journal of Affective Disorders, 246*, 480–485. https://doi.org/10.1016/j.jad.2018.12.101

ABOUT THE AUTHOR

Dr Emma Goodall is an experienced educational consultant, researcher, author and public speaker. Dr Goodall is a qualified teacher with 15 years' experience in classroom teaching, prior to training preservice teachers and entering into educational consultancy. Dr Goodall is also a qualified practicing life coach, meditation and mindfulness teacher. Through her research into interoception and collaboration with a wide range of educators and health professionals she has been able to help a significant number of children in hundreds of schools and preschools in Australia and New Zealand. Dr Goodall's other books can be found online and in bookstores as well as her website https://mindfuulbodyawareness.com

CPSIA information can be obtained
at www.ICGtesting.com
Printed in the USA
LVHW071405241119
638068LV00031B/1299/P